TYPICALLY TOPICAL
QUIZZES

First published in 2003 by Miles Kelly Publishing Ltd,
Bardfield Centre, Great Bardfield, Essex, CM7 4SL

ISBN 1-84236-280-1

2 4 6 8 10 9 7 5 3 1

Project Manager: Ruthie Boardman
Cover Design: Guy Rodgers

Contact us by email: info@mileskelly.net
Check our website and purchase other Miles Kelly products:
www.mileskelly.net

Printed in Italy

TYPICALLY TOPICAL QUIZZES

by
Christopher Rigby

Miles Kelly
PUBLISHING

About the Author

Born in Blackburn, Lancashire in 1960, Christopher Rigby has been compiling and presenting pub quizzes for the past 15 years. When he is not adding to his material for quizzes, Christopher works in the car industry. He is married to Clare – they have two teenage daughters, Hollie and Ashley and share their home with two demented dogs called Vespa and Bailey. A keen Manchester United fan Christopher lists his heroes as George Best and Homer Simpson.

TYPICALLY TOPICAL QUIZZES EXPLAINED

The following quiz book contains 90 different quizzes on 90 different topics. Whatever your speciality subject may be, it is sure to be covered in this book with topics ranging from the USA to the UK and from People and Places to Criminal Cases.

Have a go at the example below!

PHOBIAS

1. What is zoophobia the fear of? (Animals)
2. Which character, played on film by Harrison Ford, suffered from ophidiophobia (Indiana Jones)
3. Which nursery rhyme character is arachnophobic (Little Miss Muffet)

Simple Starters

....

A round of general knowledge to ease you in.

1. Divorced, beheaded, died, divorced, beheaded, survived. What does this sequence refer to?

2. In what month is St Georges Day in the UK?

3. What was the name of the Governor of Judea who ordered the crucifixion of Jesus Christ?

4. What is the largest Scandinavian country by area?

5. What type of rodent would you associate with the collective nickname of Frank Sinatra, Peter Lawford, Joey Bishop, Sammy Davis Jnr and Dean Martin?

6. What was the monetary value of the first ever stamp issued in the UK?

7. What is the name of the river that runs alongside Luxor temple?

8. Which movie star married Prince Rainier of Monaco in 1956?

9. Which Beatles single is also the name of a street in Liverpool?

10. HI is the zip code of which US state?

ANSWERS

1. The six wives of Henry VIII 2. April 3. Pontius Pilate 4. Sweden 5. Rat ie The Rat Pack 6. Penny 7. The River Nile 8. Grace Kelly 9. 'Penny Lane' 10. Hawaii

Abracadabra

....

A magical mystery tour of questions.

1. Which American magician shares his name with the favourite literary character of Charles Dickens?

2. Who played Saruman the Sorcerer in the 2001 film *The Lord Of The Rings*?

3. Who composed *The Magic Flute*?

4. 'Black Magic Woman' was the first chart entry for which pop group?

5. Which organisation was founded in Pinoli's restaurant in London in the summer of 1905?

6. In which 1993 film did Bette Midler play an evil witch?

7. How is the literary character of Digory Kirke also known in the title of a novel by C S Lewis?

8. Who wrote the black magic novels *The Devil Rides Out* and *The Satanist*?

9. Who played the title role in the 1970s American TV series *The Magician*?

10. Which 11th-century wizard, created by Richard Carpenter, found himself trapped in the 20th century on Hexwood Farm?

ANSWERS
1. David Copperfield 2. Christopher Lee 3. Mozart 4. Fleetwood Mac 5. The Magic Circle 6. *Hocus Pocus* 7. The Magician's Nephew 8. Dennis Wheatley 9. Bill Bixby 10. Catweazle

Money Matters

....

A question of cash.

1. Which fraction is also the popular name for an American 25 cent coin?

2. Which Manchester pop group's first hit was entitled 'Money's Too Tight To Mention'?

3. Which building features on the back of an American $20 bill?

4. Which cathedral features on the back of an English £20 note when Edward Elgar is on the front?

5. What currency is shared by Tunisia, Libya, Jordan and Sudan?

6. In which country do 100 satang make 1 baht?

7. How many US dollars is a sawbuck worth?

8. In what year did the farthing cease to be legal tender in Britain?

9. Which 1956 film features the song 'Who Wants To Be A Millionaire'?

10. The head of a centurion is depicted on which credit card?

ANSWERS

1. Quarter 2. Simply Red 3. The White House 4. Worcester Cathedral 5. Dinar 6. Thailand 7. 10 dollars 8. 1960 9. *High Society* 10. American Express

Animal Antics

A beast of a round.

1. What name is shared by the young of a beaver and the young of a squirrel?
2. What is the heaviest land animal after an elephant?
3. From what breed of goat is mohair obtained?
4. What is the three-letter word for a group of kangaroos?
5. Who created the character of Peter Rabbit?
6. What bird lays the largest egg in comparison to the size of its body?
7. Nipper the dog is the trademark of which record label?
8. Bluefin, Bonito and yellowfin are all species of which fish?
9. What eight-letter S word is the name given to the nasal opening of a whale?
10. To which animal family do giant pandas belong?

ANSWERS

1. Kitten 2. Hippopotamus 3. Angora goat 4. Mob 5. Beatrix Potter 6. Kiwi 7. His Master's Voice 8. Tuna 9. Spiracle 10. Raccoon

Body Wise

Which parts of the body are affected by the diseases below?

1. Hepatitis
2. Dermatitis
3. Meningitis
4. Gingivitis
5. Pneumonia
6. Lumbago
7. Cystitis
8. Haemophilia
9. Conjunctivitis
10. Phlebitis

ANSWERS

1. Liver 2. Skin 3. Brain 4. Gums 5. Lungs 6. The lower back 7. Bladder 8. Blood 9. Eyes 10. Veins

All Dressed Up

Clothes conundrums!

1. Which former member of the Q Tips had a solo hit with 'Wherever I Lay My Hat, That's My Home'?
2. What fabric was named after Nimes in France?
3. Worn by Russian peasant women, what is a babushka?
4. In which sport do participants wear a hat called a montero?
5. Was the article of clothing the cardigan named after a bay, an earl or a breed of cattle?
6. In which 1990 film did Eric Idle and Robbie Coltrane don wimples?
7. Which Italian fashion designer rose to fame after supplying the wardrobe for Richard Gere in the film *American Gigolo*?
8. The Dolly Varden hat was named after a character in which Dickens novel?
9. What was the real first name of fashion designer Coco Chanel?
10. Who wrote the novel *The Man In The Iron Mask*?

ANSWERS

1. Paul Young 2. Denim 3. Headscarf 4. Bullfighting, the black hat worn by matadors 5. An earl 6. *Nuns On The Run* 7. Giorgio Armani 8. *Barnaby Rudge* 9. Gabrielle 10. Alexandre Dumas

Literary Logic

....

For the bookworms.

1. Fans of which literary character belong to an organisation called The Baker Street Irregulars?

2. The Thane of Glamis is the title held by which Shakespeare character?

3. John Blackthorne is the central character of which novel, who has been played on film by Richard Chamberlain?

4. Which county do Ma and Pa Larkin call home in *The Darling Buds Of May*?

5. In which country did the Pied Piper play his pipes in the town of Hamelin?

6. Which Ian Fleming novel tells the story of a plot to rob Fort Knox?

7. What is the first name of the prince in Mark Twain's novel, *The Prince And The Pauper*?

8. By what six-letter name is John Clayton known in a number of books?

9. What surname links the authors of *Tom Jones* and *Bridget Jones's Diary*?

10. What breed of terrier dog was named after a character in the Walter Scott novel *Guy Mannering*?

ANSWERS
1. Sherlock Holmes 2. Macbeth 3. *Shogun* 4. Kent 5. Germany 6. *Goldfinger* 7. Edward 8. Tarzan 9. Fielding 10. Dandie Dimont

Let's Dance

Waltz your way to the answers.

1. Which song won a Best Song Oscar for the film *Dirty Dancing*?

2. Which composer's life story was chronicled in the film *The Waltz King*?

3. Which pop group was 'Twisting By The Pool' in 1983?

4. What word represents the letter F in the phonetic alphabet?

5. Constant Billy, Ampleforth and Adderburg are all types of what dance?

6. Which film star was born Virginia McMath?

7. Which 1969 film starring Jane Fonda told the story of a marathon dance contest?

8. The mazurka is the national dance of which European country?

9. What animated birds did Dick Van Dyke dance with in the film *Mary Poppins*?

10. Which 1985 film told the story of Ruth Ellis, the last woman to be hanged in Britain?

ANSWERS
1. 'Time Of My Life' 2. Johann Strauss 3. Dire Straits 4. Foxtrot 5. Morris dance 6. Ginger Rogers 7. *They Shoot Horses Don't They* 8. Poland 9. Penguins 10. *Dance With A Stranger*

Capital A's

....

Name the capitals of the following, all of which begin with the letter A.

1. Greece
2. Paraguay
3. Netherlands
4. Maine
5. Turkey
6. Ghana
7. Ethiopia
8. Jordan
9. Nigeria
10. Madagascar

2002

How much do you know about events of 2002?

1. Set in India, what is the title of the Andrew Lloyd Webber musical that opened in the West End in June 2002?

2. Which Aston Villa striker scored on his England debut in February 2002?

3. Which actor known for playing *Rumpole of the Bailey* died in July 2002?

4. In January 2002 the town of Goma was engulfed by a volcanic eruption. In which African Republic is Goma?

5. Which former Wimbledon champion fell foul of the taxman in 2002 when investigated in an alleged £5 million tax fraud?

6. A seven-foot statue of which man was unveiled at Liverpool's airport in March 2002?

7. Which member of the British royal family died aged 71 in 2002?

8. Which capital of the Czech Republic was flooded in August 2002?

9. Which Premiership football manager received a knighthood in 2002?

10. In which country did Pope John Paul II deliver the largest ever open-air mass in August 2002?

ANSWERS

1. *Bombay Dreams* 2. Darius Vassell 3. Leo McKern 4. Democratic Republic of Congo 5. Boris Becker 6. John Lennon 7. Princess Margaret 8. Prague 9. Sir Bobby Robson 10. Poland

Lion Logic

Feline facts on the King of the Jungle.

1. Which literary land was ruled by Aslan the lion?
2. Which king did Peter O'Toole play in *The Lion In Winter*?
3. In the Bible, who was cast into the lion's den?
4. Who wrote of Elsa the lioness in the novel *Born Free*?
5. In which month does the star sign of Leo begin?
6. Which football hero of yesteryear was nicknamed The Lion Of Vienna?
7. Which African country has a name that means Lion Mountains?
8. Leo the lion appears in the opening credits of which film company's movies?
9. What was the name of the cross-eyed lion in the 60s TV series *Daktari*?
10. Which English football club are nicknamed The Lions?

ANSWERS

1. Narnia 2. Henry II 3. Daniel 4. Joy Adamson 5. July 6. Nat Lofthouse 7. Sierra Leone 8. MGM 9. Clarence 10. Millwall

Name That Year

Identify the years from the clues given.

In what year...

1. Did the nuclear disaster at Chernobyl take place?
2. Did Kate Winslett star in the film *Titanic*?
3. Was the Treaty of Versailles signed?
4. Of the 1980s saw the first Papal visit to Britain for 450 years?
5. Did the sixpence cease to be legal tender in the UK?
6. Was the singer Robbie Williams born?
7. Did Lennox Lewis make his professional boxing debut?
8. Did the US government approve the sales of Viagra?
9. Was Lee Harvey Oswald assassinated by Jack Ruby?
10. Did Keith Moon of The Who die?

Ring The Bell

Ding Dong dilemmas!

1. The Liberty Bell March by John Sousa was the theme music for which TV comedy show?
2. Who released the best-selling album *Tubular Bells*?
3. Who created the literary bell ringer Quasimodo?
4. Which Edinburgh-born inventor was President of the National Geographic Society from 1896 to 1904?
5. In the nursery rhyme Oranges and Lemons, which bells say, 'When will you pay me'?
6. In which 1978 film did Sting play a bellboy?
7. What is a *campanile*?
8. What is the name of the bell at Lloyds of London rung in times of disaster?
9. During which 1930s conflict was the novel *For Whom The Bell Tolls* set?
10. To be considered a true Cockney a person must have been born within the sound of which bells?

ANSWERS

1. *Monty Python's Flying Circus* 2. Mike Oldfield 3. Victor Hugo 4. Alexander Graham Bell 5. The Bells of Old Bailey 6. *Quadrophenia* 7. A bell tower 8. Lutine Bell 9. Spanish Civil War 10. Bow bells

Science Fact

For the Einsteins of the world.

1. P is the chemical symbol for which element?
2. What name is given to the full moon that is nearest to the Autumn Equinox?
3. What is the name of the hormone that stimulates the nervous system and raises the heart rate?
4. Which planet of the solar system was originally named after George III?
5. Is graminology the study of words, grass, weights, flags or lakes?
6. What is the only chemical element to be named after a state of the USA?
7. By what shorter name is trichlorophenol better known?
8. In the world of physics, what do the initials UV stand for?
9. Which is the only chemical element beginning with the letter U?
10. Which hormone is responsible for regulating blood sugar levels?

ANSWERS

1. Phosphorus 2. Harvest moon 3. Adrenalin 4. Uranus 5. Grass 6. Californium 7. TCP 8. Ultra violet 9. Uranium 10. Insulin

Crack The Codes

Identify the American states from their zip codes.

1. MD
2. GA
3. AR
4. IA
5. TN
6. MN
7. OH
8. NH
9. VT
10. NB

Horses For Courses

Horsing around with questions.

1. Which horse won the Aintree Grand National in 2002?
2. What is the female equivalent of a colt?
3. Who wrote the novel *Black Beauty*?
4. Which part of the intestine is shaped like a horseshoe?
5. Which group had a hit with the song, 'A Horse With No Name' in 1972?
6. Which English monarch died after falling from a horse called Sorrel?
7. In Britain, what is the name of the horse-racing organisation with which racing colours must be registered annually?
8. Who wrote the novel *The Horse Whisperer*?
9. Which Norse god rode an eight-legged horse called Sleipner?
10. Which classic novel features a horse called Boxer?

ANSWERS
1. Bindaree 2. Filly 3. Anna Sewell 4. Duodenum 5. America 6. William III 7. Weatherby's 8. Nicholas Evans 9. Odin 10. *Animal Farm*

Around England

An English test.

1. In which University City was Olivia Newton John born in 1948?
2. What is the name of the tower within the Houses Of Parliament that houses Big Ben?
3. In which building was the Great Exhibition of 1851 held?
4. In 2000 a major art centre was opened in Salford, Manchester, dedicated to which artist?
5. In which county is the town of Axminster, famed for its manufacture of carpets?
6. Which airport was opened by Queen Elizabeth II in 1958?
7. Which of the following is a disease of poultry: is it Carlisle disease, Newcastle disease or Scarborough disease?
8. In 2002 who did Lincoln City FC play in the first ever Lincolnshire derby in the Football League?
9. What is the closest bridge to the Houses of Parliament?
10. In which city is the grave of the writer Jane Austen?

ANSWERS
1. Cambridge 2. St Stephen's Tower 3. Crystal Palace 4. L S Lowry 5. Devon 6. Gatwick 7. Newcastle disease 8. Boston United 9. Westminster Bridge 10. Winchester

Bed Time

A sleepy session of questions.

1. In which 1990 film was Julia Robert terrorised by Patrick Bergin?

2. Who is the Greek God of dreams?

3. Which pop group with a female lead vocalist had a 1981 hit with the song, 'I Go To Sleep'?

4. Who directed the 1984 film *A Nightmare On Elm Street*?

5. Who created the sleepy literary character of Rip Van Winkle?

6. Which colourful pop group released the album, *On The Threshold Of A Dream*?

7. Which Disney film features the song, 'Once Upon A Dream'?

8. Who wrote the novel *The Big Sleep*?

9. What is the technical term for a sleepwalker?

10. In which 1989 film did Kevin Costner play Ray Kinsella and Burt Lancaster play Dr Moonlight Graham?

ANSWERS
1. *Sleeping With The Enemy* 2. Morpheus 3. The Pretenders 4. Wes Craven 5. Washington Irving 6. Moody Blues 7. *Sleeping Beauty* 8. Raymond Chandler 9. Somnambulist 10. *Field Of Dreams*

A Driving Test

Which countries have the following international car registration plates?

1. KWT
2. EC
3. BG
4. L
5. B
6. RA
7. BD
8. JA
9. LB
10. AL

Food For Thought

....

A tasty round of trivia.

1. What name is given to an animal's pancreas when used as food?

2. According to the proverb, he was a brave man that first ate a what?

3. January, Arctic King and Savoy are all varieties of which vegetable?

4. In an Indian restaurant, what are aloo?

5. In which city did the Waldorf salad originate?

6. Jasmine and long grain are both types of what?

7. In the ancient world what item of food symbolised eternity, due to its many layers?

8. What is the connection between the towns of Eccles, Banbury and Dundee?

9. In Indian cuisine, what five-letter word is a cooking instruction meaning 'to braise'?

10. In Austria, what name is given to a breaded veal cutlet?

ANSWERS

1. Sweetbread 2. Oysters 3. Cabbage 4. Potatoes 5. New York 6. Rice 7. Onion 8. All gave their names to types of cake 9. Korma 10. Wiener schnitzel

Presidential Posers

....

How well do you know your American Presidents?

1. Which political party was led by George Washington?

2. What is the middle name of Bill Clinton, which was also the last name of the third US President?

3. Which President of the USA has been portrayed most often on film?

4. During the 20th century were there more Republican or Democratic Presidents?

5. Which US President, who held office from 1953 to 1961, had a golfing trophy named after him?

6. In 2001 who did George W Bush appoint as his Vice President?

7. Who was President of the USA throughout World War I?

8. Who was sworn in as President on an aeroplane following the assassination of John F Kennedy?

9. What does the D stand for in the name of Franklin D Roosevelt?

10. Which former President who died in 1994 was the only President to be born in California?

ANSWERS
1. Federalist 2. Jefferson 3. Abraham Lincoln 4. Republican 5. Dwight Eisenhower
6. Richard Cheney 7. Woodrow Wilson 8. Lyndon B Johnson 9. Delano
10. Richard Nixon

The Choice Is Yours

A multiple choice round.

1. Does the adjective 'anguine' refer to snakes, eagles or goats?
2. Is T positive the blood group of Dr Who, Mr Spock or Darth Vader?
3. Is S the chemical symbol for sodium, sulphur or silicon?
4. Is St Florian the patron saint of policemen, nurses or firemen?
5. Who once performed under the name Tom & Jerry, was it Simon & Garfunkel, the Righteous Brothers or Sonny & Cher?
6. Is Sexton Blake cockney rhyming slang for cake, steak or fake?
7. Is Planet Deep the deepest point of the Indian Ocean, the Atlantic Ocean or the Arctic Ocean?
8. Is a *ghaghra* a shirt, a skirt or a hat?
9. Is 2002 the Chinese year of the dragon, the rabbit or the horse?
10. Was the artist John Constable born in the 17th century, the 18th century or the 19th century?

ANSWERS
1. Snakes 2. Mr Spock 3. Sulphur 4. Firemen 5. Simon & Garfunkel 6. Fake 7. Indian Ocean 8. Skirt 9. Horse 10. 18th century

3

Three Of A Kind

Ten questions, all of which require three answers.

1. What is the oldest university in England, Scotland and Ireland?
2. Which three EU countries did not adopt the Euro as their currency on January 1, 2002?
3. Name the three actors who on film formed a company known as The Ghostbusters.
4. Which three animals with three letters in their name are used to represent Chinese years?
5. At Wimbledon 2002 who were the top three ranked British male tennis players?
6. Which three countries beginning with the letter P played in football's World Cup finals in 2002?
7. Name the three towns or cities where the Tate Gallery has branches in England.
8. Name the first three South African golfers to win the US Open.
9. In which three films directed by Alfred Hitchcock did Grace Kelly have a starring role?
10. What are the first three cities to be mentioned in the lyrics of the song 'Dancing In The Street'?

ANSWERS
1. Oxford University, St Andrews and Queens University 2. UK, Denmark and Sweden 3. Dan Aykroyd, Bill Murray and Harold Ramis 4. Dog, rat and pig 5. Tim Henman, Greg Rusedski and Martin Lee 6. Portugal, Paraguay and Poland 7. London, Liverpool and St Ives 8. Gary Player, Ernie Els and Retief Goosen 9. Dial M For Murder, To Catch A Thief and Rear Window 10. Chicago, New Orleans and New York

28

A History Lesson

A trivia trek through time.

1. Robert the Bruce defeated the English at which battle?
2. Who did Elizabeth II succeed as British monarch?
3. Which country was ruled by the Ptolemies in ancient times?
4. Nelson's Column in London commemorates which battle?
5. Who was the longest-reigning British King?
6. The Tet Offensive marked the beginning of the end of which war?
7. Which nation were Britain's opponents in The Hundred Years War?
8. Which empire was destroyed by the Spanish invasion of Mexico in the 16th century?
9. In which city was the Archbishop Thomas Beckett murdered?
10. What R word is the name given to the period in history directly after the demise of Cromwell's Protectorate?

ANSWERS
1. Battle of Bannockburn 2. George VI 3. Egypt 4. Battle of Trafalgar 5. George III 6. Vietnam War 7. France 8. Aztec 9. Canterbury 10. Restoration

From English To American

What are the American equivalents of the following English words?

1. Nappy
2. Car bonnet
3. Autumn
4. Paraffin
5. Tap
6. Braces (as in trousers)
7. Truncheon
8. Crisps
9. Drawing pin
10. Courgette

Just James

Identify the famous men called James from the clues given.

1. Which movie icon was buried in Fairmount, Indiana on October 8, 1955 aged just 24?

2. Which infamous criminal born in 1847 was a member of the Confederate guerrilla group known as the Quantrills?

3. Who wrote the novel *The Secret Life Of Walter Mitty*?

4. *Unreliable Memoirs* is the title of the autobiography of which Sidney-born broadcaster?

5. Which Belfast-born musician is known as The Man With The Golden Flute?

6. Which 18th-century weaver invented the Spinning Jenny?

7. Who connects the films *Ragtime*, *Public Enemy* and *Angels With Dirty Faces*?

8. Who won the Formula One World Championship in 1976 and died in 1993?

9. Who directed the films *Terminator*, *True Lies* and *The Abyss*?

10. Who was the fifth President of the USA?

ANSWERS
1. James Dean 2. Jesse James 3. James Thurber 4. Clive James 5. James Galway 6. James Hargreaves 7. James Cagney 8. James Hunt 9. James Cameron 10. James Monroe

3

Body Matters

....

A trivia test on the human body.

1. What D word is the name given to the calcified tissue of teeth?
2. Which side of the brain is the rational side?
3. Which part of the eye controls the size of the pupil?
4. Where in the human body is the carotid artery?
5. What is known as The Kissing Disease?
6. What is the largest gland in the human body?
7. What is the more common four-letter name for the olfactory organ?
8. How many pairs of ribs do humans have?
9. What kind of transplant was first successfully carried out by Dr Richard Lawler in 1950?
10. What is removed in an operation known as a tenotomy?

ANSWERS
1. Dentine 2. Left 3. Iris 4. Neck 5. Glandular fever 6. Liver 7. Nose 8. 12 9. Kidney transplant 10. Tendon

32

Football Crazy

How well do you know your football facts?

1. Which London football club won the FA Cup in 1975 fielding a team of eleven English players?
2. Which club did Manchester United sell striker Dwight Yorke to in 2002?
3. Which electronics company sponsors the Dutch football club, PSV Eindhoven?
4. Which Catholic footballer was involved in a controversial transfer to Rangers in 1989?
5. In the 2002/2003 season, which phone company sponsored Arsenal Football Club?
6. Which Italian Serie A football club play their home matches in the town of Bergamo?
7. Portman Road is the home ground of which club?
8. Who was the heaviest player in England's 2002 World Cup squad?
9. Which football club were formerly called West Herts?
10. In which city is a derby match contested between the Blades and the Owls?

ANSWERS
1. West Ham United 2. Blackburn Rovers 3. Philips 4. Mo Johnston 5. O2 6. Atalanta 7. Ipswich Town 8. David Seaman 9. Watford 10. Sheffield

The Final Countdown

In the given years name the singers or groups that recorded the hit singles below.

1. 1981 – 'One In Ten'
2. 1980 – '9 To 5'
3. 1966 – 'Eight Miles High'
4. 1974 – 'The Seven Seas Of Rye'
5. 1974 – 'The Six Teens'
6. 1982 – 'Just Who Is The Five O'clock Hero'
7. 1988 – 'Four Letter Word'
8. 1960 – 'Three Steps To Heaven'
9. 1988 – 'Two Hearts'
10. 1979 – 'One Step Beyond'

ANSWERS

1. UB40 2. Sheena Easton 3. The Byrds 4. Queen 5. Sweet 6. The Jam 7. Kim Wilde 8. Eddie Cochran 9. Phil Collins 10. Madness

34

A Tour Of Europe

A trivia trek through Europe.

1. On which river does the city of Cologne stand?
2. What is the largest island in Europe?
3. What stretches from the Gulf of Genoa to the city of Vienna?
4. Helvetia was the Roman name of which European country?
5. What is the capital city of Finland?
6. What is the official language of San Marino?
7. Which river has a name that means 'River of sheep'?
8. What is the name of the summer residence of the French President?
9. Cape St Vincent can be found at the South-west tip of which country?
10. Which European country boasts the world's oldest national flag?

Your Number's Up!!

Answers that add up.

1. What is the only number that has the same number of letters as its value?

2. What is the most popular finishing double for professional darts players?

3. What is the title of the film sequel to *Three Men And A Baby*?

4. Of the fifty American states, how many were established in the 20th century?

5. In computer terminology, how many bits are in a byte?

6. How many years of marriage are celebrated for a Pearl Anniversary?

7. Up to 2002, how many Presidents of the USA have been called William?

8. What is a gross minus a score?

9. What number preceded Charing Cross Road to provide the title of a 1987 film starring Anthony Hopkins?

10. How many planets in the solar system are larger than Earth?

ANSWERS

1. Four 2. Sixteen 3. *Three Men And A Little Lady* 4. Five: Hawaii, Alaska, Arizona, New Mexico and Oklahoma 5. Eight 6. Thirty 7. Three: Clinton, Taft and Harrison 8. 124 (144-20) 9. 84 10. Four: Jupiter, Saturn, Uranus and Neptune

Watching The Detectives

Solve the clues for this detective quiz.

1. On which island did Bergerac do his detecting?

2. Who was assisted by a detective called Paul Drake and a secretary called Della Street?

3. Which US TV series featured the character of Sergeant Pepper Anderson?

4. Which TV detective lived in a trailer and kept his gun in a biscuit tin?

5. Who created the medieval detective Brother Cadfael?

6. Set in Honolulu, which TV series featured Detective Danny Williams?

7. Who created the aristocratic sleuth Lord Peter Wimsey?

8. Name the actor who plays Andy Sipowicz in *NYPD Blue*.

9. Which Hollywood sex symbol played a police detective called David Mills in the film *Seven*?

10. What is the name of the detective agency in the TV series *Moonlighting*?

4

A Whale Of A Time

How much do you know about whales?

1. What is the name of the ferocious whale in the Disney cartoon *Pinocchio*?

2. In the Bible, who was swallowed by a whale?

3. *Orcinus Orca* is the Latin name for what?

4. Who wrote the novel *Moby Dick*?

5. Who played Captain Ahab in the 1956 film version of *Moby Dick*?

6. What is the largest species of whale?

7. What was the name of the whale released back into the wild after appearing in the *Free Willy* films?

8. Who directed the 1931 film *Frankenstein*?

9. What is the name of the substance found in the intestines of sperm whales that is added to perfume to slow down the rate of evaporation?

10. What species of whale was central to the plot of the film *Star Trek IV*?

ANSWERS
1. Monstro 2. Jonah 3. Killer whale 4. Herman Melville 5. Gregory Peck 6. Blue whale 7. Keiko 8. James Whale 9. Ambergris 10. Humped back whale

Pick Of The Pops

A round of pop posers.

1. In which country was Gloria Estefan born?

2. Where did The Beatles 'rent a cottage' according to the lyrics of the song 'When I'm Sixty-Four'?

3. Which singer was the best man at the 1986 wedding of Bob Geldof and Paula Yates?

4. Which 60s pop group had a female drummer called Ann Lantree?

5. In what year did country and western singer John Denver die in a plane crash?

6. Which classical composer originally composed the music on which the pop song 'A Whiter Shade Of Pale' is based?

7. Which TV pop music show of the 1960s informed the viewers, 'The weekend starts here'?

8. Mark, Christian, Paul and Ben are the members of which boy band?

9. Which punk rocker was born William Broad?

10. Which cartoon character's name did Orville Burrell adopt as his stage name?

ANSWERS
1. Cuba 2. The Isle of Wight 3. Simon Le Bon 4. The Honeycombs 5. 1997 6. J S Bach 7. Ready, Steady, Go 8. A1 9. Billy Idol 10. Shaggy

A Mixed Salad

Identify the fruit or vegetables from each group of three varieties below.

1. Arran Victory, Cyprus and Desiree
2. Alicante, Red Alert and Tiny Tim
3. Cos, Arctic King and Density
4. Conference, Bartlett and Williams
5. Halawi, Morello and Zahidi
6. Semillon, Cardinal and Cassidy
7. Blenheim, Russet and Granny Smith
8. Little Marvel, Shaft and petit pois
9. Early Giant, Figaro and Autumn King
10. Pecan, Pine and Beech

ANSWERS
1. Potato 2. Tomato 3. Lettuce 4. Pear 5. Cherry 6. Grape 7. Apple 8. Pea 9. Carrot
10. Nut

Wet Wet Wet

A quiz with a watery theme.

1. Which of Africa's great rivers discharges into the Gulf of Guinea in the Atlantic Ocean?

2. What is the world's largest bay?

3. Who wrote the novel *Ring Of Bright Water*?

4. Turkey and Bulgaria both form a coastline on which sea?

5. What nationality is the composer who wrote *The Water Music*?

6. In which London park is there a lake known as The Serpentine?

7. Which 1970 album included the tracks, 'I Am A Rock' and 'Homeward Bound'?

8. On which river does the French city of Nantes stand?

9. The river Volga, the longest river in Europe, discharges into which sea?

10. In which film is the Deacon the villainous leader of the Smokers?

ANSWERS
1. Niger 2. Hudson Bay 3. Gavin Maxwell 4. Black Sea 5. German (Handel) 6. Hyde Park 7. *Bridge Over Troubled Water* 8. Loire 9. Caspian Sea 10. *Waterworld*

People Posers

Ten teasers on famous people.

1. In 1998 who released an album entitled *The Violin Player*?
2. What was the nationality of the first man to reach the South Pole?
3. Whose statue stands in front of the British Embassy in Washington DC?
4. What connects the British monarchs Edward II, Edward VIII and Richard II?
5. Which novelist had the first names of Herbert Ernest?
6. *I Remember It Well* is the title of the autobiography of which French entertainer?
7. In which country was Cleopatra born?
8. Who composed the opera *The Flying Dutchman*?
9. Which car company was founded by Sir William Lyons in 1922?
10. What is the connection between Jerry Lee Lewis, Charlie Chaplin and Bill Wyman?

ANSWERS
1. Vanessa Mae 2. Norwegian 3. Winston Churchill 4. They all abdicated 5. HE Bates 6. Maurice Chevalier 7. Greece 8. Richard Wagner 9. Jaguar 10. They all married teenage brides

For The Bird Brains

Test your knowledge with these feathery facts.

1. What is the largest bird native to Great Britain?

2. What is the nickname of Brighton Football Club?

3. Who played the title role in the 1984 film *Birdy*, directed by Alan Parker?

4. *The Birdman Of Alcatraz* was imprisoned in the bay of which city?

5. What bird known as the harbinger of spring is known for laying its eggs in the nests of other birds?

6. Who wrote the poem *Ode To A Nightingale*?

7. What species of duck is also the title of a James Bond film?

8. Which of the following is not a bird: is it jacksnipe, a godwit, a krait, a red poll or a nuthatch?

9. What species of falcon shares its name with a character from Arthurian legend?

10. Is a rafter the collective noun for a group of owls, turkeys or partridges?

ANSWERS

1. Mute swan 2. The Seagulls 3. Matthew Modine 4. San Francisco 5. Cuckoo 6. John Keats 7. Goldeneye 8. A krait, which is a snake 9. Merlin 10. Turkeys

Novel Ideas

Name the writer who penned each group of three novels.

1. *Salem's Lot, Carrie* and *The Shining*
2. *Emma, Persuasion* and *Sense And Sensibility*
3. *The BFG, Matilda* and *James And The Giant Peach*
4. *Howard's End, A Passage To India* and *A Room With A View*
5. *Jane Eyre, Villette* and *The Professor*
6. *Under The Greenwood Tree, The Mayor Of Casterbridge* and *Far From The Madding Crowd*
7. *The Fourth Estate, First Among Equals* and *Not A Penny More Not A Penny Less*
8. *Kidnapped, Catriona* and *Treasure Island*
9. *Porterhouse Blue, Wilt* and *Blott On The Landscape*
10. *Where Eagles Dare, The Guns Of Navarone* and *Ice Station Zebra*

Phobias

Do you have a fear of questions?

1. What is zoophobia the fear of?

2. What does a xenophobic person fear?

3. Which character played on film by Harrison Ford suffers from ophidiophobia?

4. What kind of weather does an astraphobic person fear?

5. What is mysophobia the fear of?

6. Which nursery rhyme character suffers from arachnophobia?

7. Is chromophobia the fear of metal, colour or chromosomes?

8. What number does a triskaidekaphobic person fear?

9. Napoleon Bonaparte suffered from ailurophobia. What animal was he afraid of?

10. What H word is an alternative name for rabies?

ANSWERS
1. Animals 2. Foreigners or foreign things 3. Indiana Jones 4. Lightning 5. Dirt 6. Little Miss Muffet 7. Colour 8. 13 9. Cats 10. Hydrophobia

45

SESSION 5

A Rodent Round

From dirty rats to Mickey Mouse!!

1. Which British horror story writer penned the novel *The Rats*?
2. What is the name of Roland Rat's gerbil companion?
3. Rat Scabies was a member of which punk rock group?
4. Which pop group had hits with the songs 'Like Clockwork' and 'Banana Republic'?
5. In which 1959 film starring Peter Sellers did the tiny Duchy of Grand Fenwick declare war on the USA?
6. Which Shakespeare play features the characters of Christopher Sly and a servant called Curtis?
7. What did Douglas Engelbart invent in 1964?
8. What is the name of Manuel's pet rat in *Fawlty Towers*?
9. What is the name of the cartoon mouse in Bart Simpson's favourite TV show?
10. What was the original name of Mickey Mouse?

ANSWERS

1. James Herbert 2. Kevin the gerbil 3. The Damned 4. Boomtown Rats 5. *The Mouse That Roared* 6. *The Taming Of The Shrew* 7. The computer mouse 8. Basil 9. Itchy 10. Mortimer

46

Collectively Speaking

What are collected by the following?

1. Bibliophile
2. Deltiologist
3. Numismatist
4. Philatelist
5. Conchologist
6. Fromologist
7. Lepidopterist
8. Arctopholist
9. Discophile
10. Oologist

ANSWERS

1. Books 2. Picture postcards 3. Coins or medals 4. Stamps 5. Seashells 6. Cheese labels 7. Butterflies or moths 8. Teddy bears 9. Gramophone records 10. Bird's eggs

Peak Practices

Scale the heights of knowledge with these mountainous questions.

1. In what year was the peak of Mount Everest first reached by Edmund Hillary and Tenzing Norgay?

2. Mount Aneto in Spain is the highest peak in which range?

3. In which 1975 film did Clint Eastwood find himself scaling the meanest mountain on Earth?

4. In which mountain range is Ben Nevis?

5. Which mountain with a biblical connection is the highest peak in Turkey?

6. Which mountain range extends from the Arctic Ocean to Kazakhstan and forms part of the border between Europe and Asia?

7. Was Mount Everest named after George Everest, Jack Everest or John Everest?

8. In which country is K2, the second highest mountain in the world?

9. In which 1993 film did Sylvester Stallone play a mountain rescue professional called Gabe Walker?

10. What is the longest mountain range in Australia?

ANSWERS
1. 1953 2. Pyrenees 3. *The Eiger Sanction* 4. The Grampians 5. Mount Ararat
6. The Urals 7. George Everest, a 19th-century Surveyor General of India 8. Pakistan
9. *Cliffhanger* 10. The Great Dividing Range

For The Telly Addicts

A TV trivia test.

1. Carrie, Samantha, Charlotte and Miranda are the four main characters in which US TV drama?

2. Which short-lived soap was set in the resort of Los Barros?

3. Which TV police detective lived on a boat called the *St Vitus Dance*?

4. Who does John Shea play in the *New Adventures Of Superman*?

5. Who plays the role of Patrick Trench, the sarcastic neighbour of Victor Meldrew in *One Foot In The Grave*?

6. Who does Mork report at the end of each episode of *Mork & Mindy*?

7. Name the actor who plays Tony Soprano in the Mafia drama *The Sopranos*.

8. In which long-running sitcom did Edward Sinclair play the Verger of St Aldhelm's Church?

9. Which US sitcom featured a bank manager called Mr Drysdale?

10. The Draconians are the archenemies of which space-age hero?

ANSWERS
1. *Sex And The City* 2. *El Dorado* 3. Sonny Crockett in *Miami Vice* 4. Lex Luthor 5. Angus Deayton 6. Orson 7. James Gandolfini 8. *Dad's Army* 9. *The Beverly Hillbillies* 10. *Buck Rogers*

Hard On The Bard

Name the Shakespeare plays from which groups of three characters appear.

1. Ophelia, King Claudius and Queen Gertrude
2. Rosalind, Duke Frederick and Touchstone
3. Captain Gower, The Duke of Clarence and the Constable of France
4. The Duke of Albany, Oswald and Goneril
5. Antonio, Shylock and Portia
6. King Duncan, Banquo and Lady Macduff
7. Master Ford, John Rugby and Mistress Quickly
8. Bianca, Iago and Desdemona
9. Titania, Nick Bottom and Oberon
10. Sebastian, Orsino and Sir Toby Belch

ANSWERS
1. Hamlet 2. As You Like It 3. Henry V 4. King Lear 5. The Merchant Of Venice 6. Macbeth 7. The Merry Wives Of Windsor 8. Othello 9. A Midsummer Night's Dream 10. Twelfth Night

Dr Who

A trivia trek on TV's Timelord.

1. Who was the first actor to play Dr Who on TV?
2. What do the initials TARDIS stand for?
3. Who played the Dr in the 1965 film *Dr Who And The Daleks*?
4. Which Dr Who actor was later seen on TV living on Scatterbrook Farm?
5. How many hearts does Dr Who have?
6. What is the name of Dr Who's home planet?
7. Who created the Daleks?
8. Who played the character of Melanie Bush, one of Dr Who's assistants?
9. What is the name of the nemesis of Dr Who, played in the series by Roger Delgado?
10. Who was the fourth actor to play Dr Who on TV?

ANSWERS
1. William Hartnell 2. Time And Relative Dimension In Space 3. Peter Cushing 4. Jon Pertwee 5. Two 6. Gallifrey 7. Terry Nation 8. Bonnie Langford 9. The Master 10. Tom Baker

Rocking All Over The World

....

A musical trivia tour.

1. Which song contains the line, 'I wanna wake up in a city that doesn't sleep'?

2. Who is the female lead singer of the pop group Texas?

3. Which Simon & Garfunkel song refers to parsley, sage, rosemary and thyme in the lyrics?

4. Which small country's national anthem is entitled 'High On The Rhine'?

5. Which 80s pop group recorded the album, *London 0 Hull 4*?

6. In a 1971 song, where did Olivia Newton-John ask her love to take a walk?

7. Who was the first Welsh female singer to have a No 1 hit in the USA?

8. In which film did Madonna sing 'Don't Cry For Me Argentina'?

9. Which rock legend had a huge worldwide hit with the song 'Voodoo Chile'?

10. Which Beatles hit contains the line, 'Jo Jo left his home in Tucson Arizona for some California grass'?

ANSWERS

1. 'New York, New York' 2. Sharleen Spiteri 3. 'Scarborough Fair' 4. Liechtenstein 5. The Housemartins 6. 'The Banks Of The Ohio' 7. Bonnie Tyler 8. *Evita* 9. Jimi Hendrix 10. 'Get Back'.

Yabba Dabba Doo

A meet-the-Flintstones quiz.

1. What is the name of Fred and Wilma Flintstone's baby daughter?

2. For which construction company does Fred Flintstone work?

3. Who played Fred in the 1994 film *The Flintstones*?

4. What is the name of the daily newspaper read by the residents of Bedrock?

5. Who played Fred's mother-in-law in the 1994 film?

6. True or false? Fred and Wilma Flintstone were the first married cartoon couple to be seen sharing a bed on TV.

7. What is the favourite sporting pastime of Fred Flintstone and Barney Rubble?

8. Who played Fred in the 2000 film *The Flintstones In Viva Rock Vegas*?

9. What is the maiden name of Wilma Flintstone?

10. The town of Bedrock is in which county?

ANSWERS
1. Pebbles 2. Rock Head And Quarry Cave Construction Company 3. John Goodman 4. *Daily Slate* 5. Elizabeth Taylor 6. True 7. Tenpin bowling 8. Mark Addy 9. Slaghoople 10. Cobblestone County

Elementary

....

Identify the chemical elements from their symbols.

1. Kr

2. Hg

3. C

4. As

5. Ni

6. K

7. Au

8. Si

9. Cl

10. Na

Four Of A Kind

Each of the following ten questions requires four answers.

1. Who are the four gospel writers in the Bible?

2. What are the first names of the four members of the Eurovision Song Contest winning group, Bucks Fizz?

3. Who were the first four actors to play James Bond on film?

4. What are the names of the four horsemen of the apocalypse?

5. Which four songs were UK chart-toppers for the glam rock group T Rex?

6. Name the first four English football clubs to lift the European Cup.

7. Name the four US Presidents who held office in the 1960s.

8. Which nations were the four semi-finalists in football's 2002 World Cup?

9. Name the four actors who played The Young Ones in the anarchic TV sitcom.

10. Other than Tony Blair, who are the only four Labour British Prime Ministers of the 20th century?

ANSWERS

1. Matthew, Mark, Luke and John 2. Mike, Bobby, Cheryl and Jay 3. Sean Connery, David Niven, George Lazenby and Roger Moore 4. War, Death, Famine and Pestilence 5. 'Hot Love', 'Get It On', 'Telegram Sam' and 'Metal Guru' 6. Manchester United, Liverpool, Nottingham Forest and Aston Villa 7. Dwight Eisenhower, John F Kennedy, Lyndon B Johnson and Richard Nixon 8. Brazil, Germany, South Korea and Turkey 9. Nigel Planer, Adrian Edmondson, Rik Mayall and Christopher Ryan 10. James Callaghan, Harold Wilson, Clement Atlee and Ramsay MacDonald

SESSION 6

Man's Best Friend

A round of canine conundrums.

1. What was the name of the first dog to be sent into outer space?
2. Who wrote the novel *The Hound Of The Baskervilles*?
3. In the *Magic Roundabout* what is Dougal the dog's favourite food?
4. The Lhasa Apso breed of dog originated in which country?
5. In the children's TV programme, what was the name of *Blue Peter's* first dog?
6. Which viral disease of dogs shares its name with water-based paint containing glue and chalk?
7. Who plays the role of Daphne in the 2002 film *Scooby Doo*?
8. In what year did the Dangerous Dogs Act come into force in the UK?
9. Who wrote the novel *The Dogs Of War*?
10. Which TV family owned a pet dog called Reckless?

It's Only Words

A vocabulary test.

1. What flower is also the name for the cross-legged position in yoga?
2. What would you be doing if your soft palate and pharynx were vibrating due to an obstruction in the nasal passage?
3. A picture of whose face is found on a vernicle?
4. Donnerstag is the German word for which day of the week?
5. How many years comprise a quinquennial?
6. What S word is the name of the receptacle into which wine tasters empty their mouths?
7. What five-letter word is the more popular name for decompression sickness?
8. Appropriately, which Gilbert & Sullivan opera is an anagram of NAME FOR SHIP?
9. What is a sailor doing when splicing the mainbrace?
10. If something is said to be volitant, what is it capable of?

ANSWERS
1. Lotus 2. Snoring 3. Jesus 4. Thursday 5. Five 6. Spittoon 7. The bends 8. HMS *Pinafore* 9. Drinking alcohol 10. Flight

Astronomical Answers

A space trivia trek.

1. What is the smallest planet in the solar system?
2. The Great Red Spot is found on which planet?
3. Who was the first British astronaut to space-walk?
4. Which planet has 15 moons named after Shakespearian characters including Juliet, Desdemona and Portia?
5. What C word is the name given to the study of the universe?
6. What title has been held by Edmund Halley, Sir Martin Rees and Sir Arnold Wolfendale?
7. What is the nearest planet to Earth?
8. What was the name of the space shuttle that exploded on January 28, 1986 killing all seven crew members?
9. What is the larger, a meteor or a meteorite?
10. What is the three-letter name of the space station that was launched by the Soviet Union in 1986?

ANSWERS

1. Pluto 2. Jupiter 3. Michael Foale 4. Uranus 5. Cosmology 6. Astronomer Royal 7. Venus 8. Challenger 9. Meteorite 10. Mir

Film Facts

A mix of movie mindbenders.

1. Which chart-topping singer made her movie debut in the film *The Delinquents*?

2. Which Buddy Holly hit record shares its title with a film starring Kathleen Turner?

3. In which 1995 film did Sandra Bullock play a computer nerd?

4. Which character has been played on film by Mel Gibson, Clark Gable and Marlon Brando?

5. What is the name of the brass band led by Pete Postlethwaite in the film *Brassed Off*?

6. In which 1998 film did Leonardo DiCaprio play twin brothers?

7. In which film did John Cleese, Michael Palin and Ronnie Corbett all play employees of a zoo?

8. Which Hollywood superstar narrated the film *Armageddon*?

9. What was Kris Kristofferson's call sign in the film *Convoy*?

10. Whose last film appearance saw him playing the creator of *Edward Scissorhands*?

ANSWERS
1. Kylie Minogue 2. *Peggy Sue Got Married* 3. *The Net* 4. Fletcher Christian
5. Grimethorpe Colliery Brass Band 6. *The Man In The Iron Mask* 7. *Fierce Creatures*
8. Charlton Heston 9. Rubber Duck 10. Vincent Price

The Anniversary Waltz

Identify the wedding anniversaries from the number of
years and initial letter of the anniversary.

1. 15 years – C
2. 70 years – P
3. 45 years – S
4. 35 years – C
5. 20 years – C
6. 55 years – E
7. 14 years – I
8. 10 years – T
9. 40 years – R
10. 5 years – W

Ten For 2000

How much do you remember about this landmark year?

1. Which bridge was opened by the Queen in May, 2000 and shut down a month later as it was swinging too much?

2. Who was Labour's official candidate for London's Mayor?

3. Which Formula One racing driver survived a plane crash in May 2000?

4. Which pop group established their own record company called Big Brother in 2000?

5. In June 2000 which organisation made news headlines after heckling Tony Blair?

6. Which star of the film *Zulu* received a knighthood in 2000?

7. What was the title of the fourth in the series of *Harry Potter* novels that was released in 2000?

8. In this year Sada Walkington became the first ever person to be voted out of which TV show?

9. What name did Catherine Zeta Jones and Michael Douglas give their first-born son?

10. Which pop superstar tied the knot at Skibo Castle on January 22, 2000?

ANSWERS
1. Millennium Bridge 2. Frank Dobson 3. David Coulthard 4. Oasis 5. Women's Institute 6. Michael Caine 7. *Harry Potter And The Goblet Of Fire* 8. *Big Brother* 9. Dylan 10. Madonna

6

Myths And Legends

A fact-finding fantasy tour.

1. Who is the King of the Fairies?
2. In Greek mythology, who was doomed to carry the world on his shoulders?
3. The Egyptian god Anubis bears the head of which animal?
4. Which creature was slain by Theseus in the labyrinth?
5. Who killed the gorgon Medusa by reflecting her image in his shield?
6. What is the name of the Roman Goddess of the Dawn?
7. What V word is the name of the handmaidens of the Norse god, Odin?
8. What sweet liquid is known as the drink of the gods?
9. Who kidnapped Helen of Troy to precipitate the Trojan War?
10. Which star sign is represented by the sons of Zeus?

Who's That Lady?

Facts about famous females.

1. Who opened her first Body Shop in Brighton in 1976?
2. In 2000 which British film star gave birth to a daughter she called Mia?
3. Which writer has the longest entry in *Who's Who*?
4. In 1990 who became the first female President of the Irish Republic?
5. In the Wild West, who was nicknamed Little Miss Sure Shot?
6. Whose first fashion boutique was called Bazaar?
7. Who wrote the novel *Lace*?
8. Who became Britain's first ever female managing director of a football league club?
9. Who sang at the funeral of Frank Sinatra despite suffering from a sore throat?
10. Which singer, born in 1932, acquired the nickname of The Gal With The Giggle In Her Voice?

6

Initial Thoughts

What does the...

1. W stand for in the name of the South African politician FW De Klerk?
2. T stand for in the name of T E Lawrence, also known as Lawrence of Arabia?
3. L stand for in the name of the painter L S Lowry?
4. J stand for in the name of the composer J S Bach?
5. C stand for in the name of the Baywatch character C J Parker?
6. D stand for in the name of the singer K D Lang?
7. J stand for in the name of the author J R R Tolkein?
8. R stand for in the name of the Dallas character J R Ewing?
9. T stand for in the name of the Star Trek character James T Kirk?
10. K stand for in the name of the writer J K Rowling?

ANSWERS
1. Willem 2. Thomas 3. Laurence 4. Johann 5. Casey 6. Dawn 7. John 8. Ross 9. Tiberius 10. Kathleen

64

The Quiz Of The Century

One question for each decade of the 20th century.

1. Which famous race was won by a Frenchman called Maurice Garin when it was first contested in July 1903?

2. Who became British Prime Minister on December 7, 1916?

3. On February 14, 1929 whose gang members were slaughtered on the St Valentine's Day massacre?

4. In 1938 who became the first male tennis player to win a Grand Slam?

5. What film festival was held for the first time in September 1946?

6. In1958 who refused to accept the Nobel Prize for literature for his novel *Dr Zhivago*?

7. Who was fatally wounded in June 1968, by an assassin named Sirhan Sirhan?

8. In February 1971, women from which European country were allowed to vote for the first time?

9. Which of the Beach Boys died in 1983?

10. In which city were the Petronas Towers opened in 1997?

ANSWERS
1. Tour De France 2. David Lloyd George 3. Bugsy Moran 4. Donald Budge 5. Cannes Film Festival 6. Boris Pasternak 7. Robert Kennedy 8. Switzerland 9. Dennis Wilson 10. Kuala Lumpur

Ice Picks

Pick your way through the cold clues.

1. Who played the role of the Ice Man in the film *Top Gun*?
2. Which gas is solidified to form dry ice?
3. Which 1958 war movie starring John Mills and Sylvia Sims was set in Libya in 1942?
4. Which rap artist was born Robert Van Winkle?
5. In which 1992 film starring Michael Douglas was an ice pick used as a murder weapon?
6. What is the capital of Iceland?
7. An iceberg is a variety of which vegetable?
8. Who won an ice dance gold medal for the UK at the 1980 Winter Olympics?
9. Reputedly, whose last words were, 'That was the best ice cream soda I ever tasted'?
10. The Blackhawks are which US city's ice hockey team?

ANSWERS

1. Val Kilmer 2. Carbon dioxide 3. *Ice Cold in Alex* 4. Vanilla Ice 5. *Basic Instinct* 6. Reykjavik 7. Lettuce 8. Robin Cousins 9. Lou Costello 10. Chicago

Also Known As

Name the following people from their nicknames.

1. Which royal was nicknamed The Virgin Queen?

2. Which German leader was nicknamed The Iron Chancellor?

3. Which industrialist was nicknamed The Father Of The Railway?

4. Which military leader was nicknamed Old Blood And Guts?

5. Which sports star was nicknamed The Louisville Lip?

6. Which film star was nicknamed Hollywood's Mermaid?

7. Which writer was nicknamed The Bard Of Ayrshire?

8. Which pilot was nicknamed The Red Baron?

9. Which bodybuilder was nicknamed The World's Most Perfectly Developed Man?

10. Which writer was nicknamed The Father Of English Poetry?

ANSWERS

1. Queen Elizabeth I 2. Otto Van Bismarck 3. George Stephenson 4. General George Patton 5. Muhammad Ali 6. Esther Williams 7. Robert Burns 8. Manfred von Richthofen 9. Charles Atlas 10. Geoffrey Chaucer

Shark Attack

A quiz with a bite!

1. What is a shark's skeleton comprised of?
2. Which song contains the line, 'When the shark bites with his teeth dear, scarlet billows start to spread'?
3. Who played police detective Tom Sharkey in the 1981 film *Sharkey's Machine*?
4. Which species of shark beginning with T has a tail that is approximately the same length as the rest of its body?
5. Who wrote the novel *Jaws*?
6. In the film adaptation of *Jaws*, who played the marine biologist Matt Hooper?
7. Which English cricket county are known as The Sharks?
8. What is the largest species of shark?
9. In which 1999 film about super-intelligent sharks did Samuel L Jackson play a financial investor called Russell Franklin?
10. What sport is played by the Sheffield Sharks?

ANSWERS
1. Cartilage 2. Mack the Knife 3. Burt Reynolds 4. Thresher 5. Peter Benchley
6. Richard Dreyfuss 7. Sussex 8. Whale Shark 9. *Deep Blue Sea* 10. Basketball

A Sporting Chance

Test your sports knowledge with these trivia teasers.

1. In 2000 who became the first teenager to record championship points in the Formula One World Championships?

2. Jane Sixsmith represented England at which sport?

3. Which club side did Mick McCarthy leave to manage the Republic of Ireland?

4. Which game, originally played with snail shells, took its name from the Latin for shell?

5. Who is the only player to have faced both Martina Navratilova and Chris Evert Lloyd in Wimbledon Singles finals?

6. The River Dee runs alongside which English horseracing course?

7. What sport is played on an area measuring 2.7 m by 1.5 m?

8. At the opening ceremony of the 2000 Sydney Olympics, which Australian sports star carried the Olympic torch over Sydney Harbour Bridge?

9. Which Italian football club was formed in memory of Guiseppe Verdi?

10. In the 2002/03 Premiership football season, name the five former England managers who managed Premiership clubs.

ANSWERS

1. Jensen Button 2. Hockey 3. Millwall 4. Conkers 5. Hana Mandlikova 6. Chester 7. Table tennis 8. Greg Norman 9. Parma 10. Kevin Keegan, Bobby Robson, Terry Venables, Graham Taylor and Glenn Hoddle

My Horse, My Horse

Whose horse was called...?

1. Black Bess
2. Marengo
3. Dapple
4. Trigger
5. White Surrey
6. Silver
7. Hercules
8. Arion
9. Incitatus
10. Diablo

ANSWERS

1. Dick Turpin 2. Napoleon Bonaparte 3. Sancho Panza 4. Roy Rogers 5. Richard III 6. The Lone Ranger 7. Steptoe & Son 8. Hercules 9. Caligula 10. The Cisco Kid

Rhyme And Reason

Relive your childhood with this nursery rhyme quiz.

1. In the nursery rhyme Oranges And Lemons, how much money are the bells of St Martins owed?
2. Who put Pussy in the well?
3. The title of which nursery rhyme is derived from the Celtic words for eight, nine and ten?
4. Who could eat no fat when his wife could eat no lean?
5. Which nursery rhyme character is said to be inspired by Mary, Queen of Scots?
6. In the rhyme Four And Twenty Blackbirds, in which room was the Queen?
7. Polly put the kettle on. Who took it off?
8. On what day of the week did Solomon Grundy die?
9. With what type of weapon was Cock Robin killed?
10. Lucy Lockett lost her pocket. Who found it?

Art For Arts Sake

Pick your way through these painting posers.

1. Who painted *Dedham Vale* and *The Haywain*?

2. What was the title of the 1978 hit record that was a tribute to the painter L S Lowry?

3. By what shorter name was the Spanish artist Domenico Theotocopoulos better known?

4. In the film *Lust For Life*, Kirk Douglas portrayed Vincent Van Gogh. Which painter did Anthony Quinn play in the same film?

5. What was the first name of the Florentine artist Botticelli?

6. What was the nationality of the painter of *The Laughing Cavalier*?

7. Which pop group had a 1975 hit with the song 'Art For Arts Sake'?

8. Sir Joshua Reynolds was the principal painter for which British monarch?

9. In which European capital city is the Munch Museum, featuring the works of Edvard Munch?

10. Which pop artist, who died in 1987, survived an assassination attempt by Valerie Solanis in 1968?

ANSWERS
1. John Constable 2. 'Matchstalk Men And Matchstalk Cats And Dogs' 3. El Greco
4. Paul Gauguin 5. Sandro 6. Dutch, the painter is Franz Hals 7. 10 CC 8. George III
9. Oslo 10. Andy Warhol

Crime And Punishment

It would be a crime to get it wrong.

1. Who was shot dead in 1945 and hung upside down next to his mistress Clara Petacci?

2. In which UK city is Barlinnie Prison?

3. Which footballer's 2002 autobiography, subtitled The Truth, landed him in trouble with football chiefs?

4. Who was the hostage boyfriend of Jill Morrel who was finally released from captivity in Lebanon in August 1991?

5. In the Bible, to which land did Cain travel after murdering Abel?

6. What B word is an alternative name for embracery?

7. Ironically, who once said, 'The ballot is stronger than the bullet' before being shot dead?

8. From which London building did the SAS rescue 26 hostages in 1980?

9. Which convicted spy escaped from Wormwood Scrubs in 1966?

10. Which of Henry VIII's wives was beheaded in 1542?

ANSWERS
1. Benito Mussolini 2. Glasgow 3. Roy Keane 4. John McCarthy 5. The Land of Nod 6. Bribery 7. Abraham Lincoln 8. The Iranian Embassy 9. George Blake 10. Catherine Howard

If I Had A Song

Name the artists who had hits with the songs in the given years.

1. 1963 – 'If I Had A Hammer'
2. 1985 – 'If I Was'
3. 1968 – 'If I Were A Carpenter'
4. 1989 – 'If You Don't Know Me By Now'
5. 1987 – 'If You Let Me Stay'
6. 1998 – 'If You Tolerate This Your Children Will Be Next'
7. 1999 – 'If I Let You Go'
8. 1979 – 'If I Said You Had A Beautiful Body Would You Hold It Against Me'
9. 1978 – 'If I Can't Have You'
10. 1986 – 'If I Could Turn Back Time'

Around The USA

An American trivia trek.

1. What is the state capital of New Mexico?
2. Which island is separated from Florida by the Florida Straits?
3. In which state is Mount Rushmore, which depicts the heads of four American Presidents?
4. Which state is bordered by Colorado, Oklahoma, Missouri and Nebraska?
5. In which city is Waikiki Beach?
6. George Bush Snr, John Quincy Adams and John F Kennedy were all born in which state?
7. Which US state is nicknamed The Cotton State?
8. What was the 18th state of the USA, named in honour of the King of France?
9. Wilmington is the largest city in which state?
10. Name the four American states with names beginning with a vowel but not ending with a vowel.

ANSWERS
1. Santa Fe 2. Cuba 3. South Dakota 4. Kansas 5. Honolulu 6. Massachusetts 7. Alabama 8. Louisiana after Louis XIV 9. Delaware 10. Utah, Oregon, Arkansas and Illinois

Movie Manoeuvres

....

A trivia test on film transport.

1. Which James Bond film ended with Roger Moore and Jane Seymour on board a train?

2. In which 1975 film did Robert Redford play a stunt pilot?

3. In which film did Susan Sarandon and Geena Davis drive a car into the Grand Canyon?

4. Which 1988 film featured a talking taxi called Benny?

5. What was *U571* as in the title of the 2000 action thriller?

6. Who played a shower ring salesman called Del Griffith in the film *Planes, Trains And Automobiles*?

7. Which 1971 film featured Gene Hackman chasing a train in his car through the streets of New York?

8. In which film was Marilyn Monroe abducted by Don Murray?

9. Which 1988 spoof movie featured the characters of Ted Striker and Captain Oveur?

10. Which cult road movie directed by Dennis Hopper featured the song 'Born To Be Wild' by Steppenwolf?

Fact Or Fiction?

Are the following facts true or false?

1. President George Washington owned pet foxhounds called Drunkard and Tipsy.

2. The Lone Ranger's mask was made from the saddle of Tonto's horse Scout.

3. Bondi Beach in Australia was named after a surfer called James Bondi.

4. In Ancient Rome it was considered a sign of leadership to be born with a crooked nose.

5. Elephants are the only mammals incapable of jumping.

6. In the comic books, Beppo was the name of Superman's dog.

7. The eye of an ostrich is bigger than its brain.

8. Barbara Millicent Roberts is the full name of Barbie doll.

9. David Bowie became the first internationally famous pop star to be arrested whilst performing on stage.

10. In 1906 Theodore Roosevelt became the first American to be awarded the Nobel Peace Prize.

ANSWERS

1. True 2. False, his mask was made from the vest of his dead brother Captain Daniel Reid 3. False 4. True 5. True 6. False, Beppo was the name of Superman's monkey 7. True 8. True 9. False, that dubious distinction belongs to Jim Morrison of The Doors 10. True, he received the prize for helping to negotiate the end of the Russo-Japanese War

Lyrical Logic

....

A question of pop on song lyrics.

1. Which song opens with the line, 'Well East coast girls are hip, I really dig those styles they wear'?

2. In the Elton John hit, where did Daniel travel to on a plane?

3. In 'A Whiter Shade Of Pale' how many Vestal Virgins were leaving for the coast?

4. In the Bangles hit 'Manic Monday', who was being 'kissed by a crystal blue Italian stream'?

5. Which song character was 'More like a beauty queen from a movie scene'?

6. Which Rolling Stones song character was 'Born in a crossfire hurricane'?

7. Which hit song asks the question, 'Can you do the fandango'?

8. Which hit for Madonna opens with the words, 'Life is a mystery'?

9. Which song contains the line, 'Over Bridge of Sighs, to rest my eyes in shades of green'?

10. Which song contains the line, 'You can't start a fire without a spark'?

ANSWERS
1.'California Girls' 2. Spain 3. Sixteen 4.Valentino 5. Billie Jean 6.'Jumping Jack Flash' 7.' Bohemian Rhapsody' 8.'Like A Prayer' 9.'Itchycoo Park' 10.'Dancing In The Dark'

Around The World

A global trivia tour.

1. What is the main tourist attraction in Ulura National Park in Australia?
2. The branches of which tree feature on the United Nations flag?
3. Which London thoroughfare extends from Marble Arch to Hyde Park Corner?
4. Chianti wine is produced in which area of Italy?
5. Where in New York is the world's largest stained glass window?
6. Sudan's only coastline stands on which sea?
7. In which Canadian city is the Jacques Cartier Bridge?
8. Which is the only country in the world that has dependencies in the Arctic and the Antarctic?
9. The Negev Desert covers approximately 60 % of which country?
10. In which English county is Wellington, from where the Duke of Wellington took his title?

ANSWERS
1. Ayers Rock 2. Olive tree 3. Park Lane 4. Tuscany 5. John F Kennedy Airport 6. Red Sea 7. Montreal 8. Norway 9. Israel 10. Somerset

Comedy Capers

How much do you know about TV sitcoms?

1. In which town is 368, Nelson Mandela House?
2. Which male sitcom character gave birth to a son called Mearth?
3. Which 70s sitcom featured a political party called the Tooting Popular Front?
4. Which US sitcom was the first to be filmed live in front of a studio audience?
5. Who plays the mother of Jennifer Saunders in *Absolutely Fabulous*?
6. Which US sitcom features a dysfunctional family called the Bundys?
7. Which British sitcom features a married couple called Sharon and Chris Theodopolopoudos?
8. Herr Flick, Colonel Van Strohm and Flying Officer Fairfax are all characters in which series?
9. Which star of Coronation Street went on to play Auntie Wainwright in *Last Of The Summer Wine*?
10. What is the name of Roseanne's daughter, played in the sitcom by Sara Gilbert?

Battle Stations

....

Which wars witnessed the following conflicts?

1. The Battle of Ypres
2. The Battle of Gettysburg
3. The Battle of Agincourt
4. The Battle of Balaklava
5. The Battle of Rorke's Drift
6. The Battle of Bunker Hill
7. The Battle of Waterloo
8. The Battle of Bosworth Field
9. The Battle of Coral Sea
10. The Battle of Jarama River

ANSWERS

1. World War I 2. The US Civil War 3. 100 Years War 4. Crimean War 5. The Zulu War
6. The American War of Independence 7. The Napoleonic War 8. The War of the Roses
9. World War II 10. The Spanish Civil War

Classical Gas

A musical mix of questions.

1. Which Italian-born composer's Requiem was played at the funeral of Diana, Princess of Wales?

2. To which family of instruments does the bassoon belong?

3. Which composer of *The Four Seasons* was nicknamed the Red Priest?

4. What year is associated with an overture by Tchaikovsky that commemorates Napoleon's retreat from Russia?

5. Which opera features the characters of Gilda, Monterone and The Duke of Mantua?

6. Which composer founded The Aldeburgh Festival in 1948?

7. The Three Choirs Festival is held at Hereford Cathedral, Worcester Cathedral and which other cathedral?

8. Which composer's life was chronicled in the film *The Song Of Norway*?

9. In which capital city was Frantz Peter Schubert born?

10. Which instrument accompanies a piano, a viola and a violin in a piano quartet?

ANSWERS
1. Guiseppe Verdi 2. Oboe 3. Antonio Vivaldi 4. 1812 5. Rigoletto 6. Benjamin Britten 7. Gloucester Cathedral 8. Edvard Grieg 9. Vienna 10. Cello

Who Am I?

People posers.

1. I was born in Canada in 1917 and became known for playing a wheelchair-bound detective and a lawyer on TV. Who am I?

2. I was born in Argentina in 1928 and executed in Bolivia in 1967 after playing a pivotal role in the Cuban revolution. Who am I?

3. I was born in September 1952 in Illinois and won my first Wimbledon Men's Singles title in 1974. Who am I?

4. I was born in the state of Washington in 1967 and died in 1994, four years after recording a best-selling album called *Nevermind* with my group Nirvana. Who am I?

5. I was born in 1552 in Devon and wrote a book entitled *History Of The World* whilst imprisoned in the Tower Of London. Who am I?

6. I was born in Liverpool in 1940 and replaced Pete Best in the line-up of a pop group. Who am I?

7. I was born in California in 1965 and from 1985 to 1989 I was married to Madonna. Who am I?

8. I was born in 1915 and in 1963 I resigned as Secretary of State for War. Who am I?

9. I was born in the Netherlands in 1606 and I painted the *Night Watch*. Who am I?

10. I was born in Northumberland in 1937 and was knighted in 1994 after winning 106 caps for England. Who am I?

Once Upon A Time

How much do you know about children's literature?

1. Which brother and sister were enticed inside a house of bread built by a wicked witch?
2. What kind of animal is Alfie in the Roald Dahl story *Esio Trot*?
3. In a famous children's novel, what did Frances Hodgson Burnett describe as, 'The sweetest most mysterious looking place any one could imagine'?
4. Which Brothers Grimm fairytale tells the story of a strange little man who helps a miller's daughter spin straw into gold for the king?
5. Who wrote the novel *Children Of The New Forest*?
6. What collective name did Enid Blyton give to the young sleuths Frederick, Bets, Pip, Larry and Daisy?
7. In which Mississippi village does Tom Sawyer live?
8. What kind of bird is Old Brown in the *Beatrix Potter* stories?
9. What is the name of the big cat bought by Hermione Granger in the *Harry Potter* books?
10. Which character in *Wind In The Willows* has a passion for motorcars?

ANSWERS
1. Hansel & Gretel 2. A tortoise, Esio Trot spelt backwards 3. *The Secret Garden* 4. *Rumpelstiltskin* 5. Captain Frederick Marryat 6. *The Five Find Outers* 7. St Petersburg 8. An owl 9. Crookshanks 10. Toad

City Links

Identify the cities from three of their landmarks.

1. Fort Denison, Centrepoint Tower and El Alamein Fountain
2. Pompidou Centre, Arc de Triomphe and the Louvre
3. NATO Headquarters, Grand Place and the Palace of Justice
4. The Cathedral Church of Our Lady, the BMW Tower and the Olympic Tower
5. The Pentagon, the Lincoln Memorial and the Library of Congress
6. Arthur's Seat, Holyrood House and the Sir Walter Scott Memorial
7. Corovado Mountain, Copacabana Beach and Sugar Loaf Mountain
8. Red Square, Gorky Park and Lenin's Mausoleum
9. Devil's Peak, Hout Bay Harbour and the Good Hope Gallery
10. The Bridge of Segovia, Plaza Mayor and Almundena Cathedral

ANSWERS
1. Sydney 2. Paris 3. Brussels 4. Munich 5. Washington DC 6. Edinburgh 7. Rio de Janeiro 8. Moscow 9. Cape Town 10. Madrid

SESSION 9

Classic TV

Test your memory on these TV shows of the past.

1. Who provided the voice of Charlie in the 70s TV show *Charlie's Angels*?

2. Which organisation's secret headquarters was located behind Del Floria's tailor shop in New York?

3. Who played the role of Paris in the TV series *Mission Impossible* but is better known for his film and TV role playing an alien?

4. Which character was played by Richard Anderson in *The Six Million Dollar Man*?

5. Which duo's boss was called Captain Harold Dobie?

6. Who played the role of Victoria Barkley in the Old West drama *The Big Valley*?

7. In which 60s sci-fi series did Dr Philips and Dr Newman travel through time?

8. Which employee of the Illinois Central Railroad was played on TV by Alan Hale Jnr?

9. Which nine-year-old boy worked as a secret agent for the World Intelligence Network?

10. Which sitcom, first shown in 1968, was set at Fenn Street School?

ANSWERS
1. John Forsythe 2. UNCLE in *The Man from UNCLE* 3. Leonard Nimoy 4. Oscar Goldman 5. *Starsky and Hutch* 6. Barbara Stanwyck 7. *The Time Tunnel* 8. Casey Jones 9. Joe 90 10. *Please Sir*

D Is For Dog

Identify the following creatures, all of which begin with the letter D.

1. What was the second bird that was released from the ark by Noah?

2. Which breed of dog was named after an Adriatic coast of Yugoslavia?

3. What name is given to a male duck?

4. What name is given to a camel with one hump?

5. What word can precede stalker and follow rein?

6. What is the better known name of a warrigal?

7. What mammal has webbed feet, a tail similar to a beaver and lays eggs?

8. Which bird, native to the island of Mauritius, was declared extinct in the late 17th century?

9. What species of beetle destructive to wood was named after the tapping sound it makes?

10. What is the alternative name for the hedge sparrow?

ANSWERS

1. Dove 2. Dalmatian 3. Drake 4. Dromedary 5. Deer 6. Dingo 7. Duck-billed platypus 8. Dodo 9. Deathwatch beetle 10. Dunnock

There's A First Time For Everything

A quiz on famous firsts.

1. In 1909 who became the first person to fly solo across the English Channel?
2. Who was the first person to win two Nobel Prizes?
3. Which comedy actor was the first man to appear on the front cover of *Playboy* magazine?
4. Which pop legend was the first person to feature on the cover of *Rolling Stone* magazine?
5. In what year did Margaret Thatcher become the first female Prime Minister of Great Britain?
6. At the beginning of the 21st century, who was the First Lady of the USA?
7. Who topped the charts in 1988 with the song 'The First Time'?
8. Who was the first British monarch to live in Buckingham Palace?
9. In 1987 who became the first female artist to be inducted into the Rock and Roll Hall of Fame?
10. In what decade was the first Miss World contest held?

ANSWERS
1. Louis Bleriot 2. Marie Curie 3. Peter Sellers 4. John Lennon 5. 1979 6. Laura Bush 7. Robin Beck 8. Queen Victoria 9. Aretha Franklin 10. 1950s (1951)

Like Sister And Brother

Identify the sister and brother pop groups from their members.

1. Wayne, Jay, Merrill, Alan, Donny and little Jimmy
2. Debbie, Kim, Joni and Kathy
3. Scott Engel, Gary Leeds and John Maus
4. Patti, Maxine and LaVerne
5. Ronald, Rudolph and O'Kelly
6. Anne, Maureen, Bernadette, Linda and Colleen
7. Nicky Stevens, Sandra Stevens, Martin Lee and Lee Sheridan
8. Siobhan Fahey and Marcella Detroit
9. Jackie, Tito, Marlon, Michael and Jermaine
10. Joy, Babs and Teddie

ANSWERS

1. The Osmonds 2. Sister Sledge 3. The Walker Brothers 4. The Andrews Sisters
5. The Isley Brothers 6. The Nolans 7. Brotherhood Of Man 8. Shakespeare's Sister
9. The Jacksons 10. The Beverley Sisters

Down On The Farm

From farmer's wives to crop circles.

1. In a nursery rhyme, what does the farmer's wife pursue with a carving knife?

2. The painting *The Haywain* is set in which county?

3. Who wrote the novel *Cold Comfort Farm*?

4. Which Cockney singer had a 1959 hit with the song 'Little White Bull'?

5. Which British monarch was known as Farmer George?

6. Who plays Mandy Dingle in *Emmerdale Farm*?

7. Which news company was introduced to cinema audiences by a crowing rooster?

8. Who had a hit record with the song 'Combine Harvester' in 1976?

9. Which former US President was the son of a peanut farmer?

10. In which 2002 film does Mel Gibson play a former priest called Graham Hess who is plagued by crop circles whilst living on a Pennsylvanian farm?

ANSWERS
1.Three blind mice 2. Suffolk 3. Stella Gibbons 4.Tommy Steele 5. George III 6. Lisa Riley 7. Pathe News 8.The Wurzels 9. Jimmy Carter 10. *Signs*

Bank Statements

Credit yourself with the answers.

1. On which thoroughfare does the Bank of England stand?
2. In which film did Gene Wilder and Richard Pryor receive prison sentences after being falsely convicted of a bank robbery?
3. What nickname was bestowed upon the gambler Joseph Holson Jagger?
4. The film *Rogue Trader* tells the story of which man who caused the collapse of Barings Bank?
5. In the *Harry Potter* books, what is the name of the bank that encourages young wizards to save?
6. Which 1991 violent movie directed by Quentin Tarantino tells the story of a botched bank robbery in flashbacks?
7. Who did Kate Hoey replace as Sports Minister in Tony Blair's government?
8. Who worked as a nanny for the Banks children on Cherry Tree Lane?
9. In which 1990 film did the character of Oda Mae Brown make a large withdrawal from a bank?
10. With regard to banks, what do the initials TESSA stand for?

ANSWERS

1. Threadneedle Street 2. *Stir Crazy* 3. The Man Who Broke The Bank At Monte Carlo 4. Nick Leeson 5. Gringotts 6. *Reservoir Dogs* 7. Tony Banks 8. Mary Poppins 9. *Ghost* 10. Tax Exempt Special Savings Account

Soap Suds

Name the TV soaps from three of their characters.

1. Mitch Cooper, Jenna Wade and Cliff Barnes
2. Ethel Skinner, Simon Wicks and Eddie Royle
3. Emma Jackson, Pippa Fletcher and Shannon Reed
4. Thomas Sweeney, Ron Dixon and Jimmy Corkhill
5. Cassandra Wilder, Emma Channing and Chase Gioberti
6. Ashley Peacock, Rosie Webster and Janice Battersby
7. Dex Dexter, Blake Carrington and Dominique Deveraux
8. Dr Gibbons, Joe Mangel and Harold Bishop
9. Archie Gibbs, Chris Hunter and Benny Hawkins
10. Dr Michael Rossi, Elliott Carson and Rodney Harrington

ANSWERS
1. *Dallas* 2. *Eastenders* 3. *Home And Away* 4. *Brookside* 5. *Falcon Crest* 6. *Coronation Street* 7. *Dynasty* 8. *Neighbours* 9. *Crossroads* 10. *Peyton Place*

92

Around The House

Name the artists who recorded the following songs in the given years.

1. 1979 – 'Video Killed The Radio Star'
2. 1993 – 'Stairway To Heaven'
3. 1970 – 'Up The Ladder To The Roof'
4. 1974 – 'I Know What I Like In My Wardrobe'
5. 1955 – 'Rock Around The Clock'
6. 1980 – 'The Bed's Too Big Without You'
7. 1980 – 'Always In The Kitchen At Parties'
8. 1980 – 'Mirror In The Bathroom'
9. 1978 – 'Hanging On The Telephone'
10. 1982 – 'Living On The Ceiling'

For The Master Minds

A tough round of trivia teasers.

1. What is the closest country on mainland Europe to the Greek island of Corfu?
2. If sand is melted with sodium carbonate and limestone what is formed?
3. Which TV series featured a submarine called the *Getacean*?
4. Diamond Joe Quimby is the mayor of which town?
5. What surname was shared by the 9th and 23rd Presidents of the USA?
6. What is the name of the Queen's bodyguard in Scotland?
7. Which building connects Oscar Wilde and the actor Stacy Keach?
8. What is the last book of the Old Testament?
9. What do somniloquists do?
10. Between 575 AD and 1922, what name was taken by fifteen Popes?

For The Mega Master Minds

An even tougher round of trivia teasers.

1. Mayonnaise was named after the capital of which island?

2. On the human body, where are the lunula?

3. Which 1998 film was a re-make of the 1934 film *Death Takes A Holiday*?

4. Which city stands at the head of Port Philip Bay?

5. What first was achieved by the brothers Daniel and Christopher Smith in 1982?

6. In the novel *The Mill On The Floss*, what is the name of the mill?

7. What is the more common name for tauromancy?

8. What nickname was bestowed upon the gangster who was born Lester Gillis?

9. How are Dusty Bottoms, Ned Nederlander and Lucky Day collectively known in the title of a 1986 film?

10. September 28, known as Teacher's Day, is an official annual holiday in Taiwan. Whose birthday does it celebrate?